Grade 1 Math

Contents

Draw a line from each word to the matching number.

Example:

three   5

five   1

two   3

six   6

one   2

Matching Number to Quantity

Count the maple leaves in each part of the beach towel.
Colour each part to match the numbered crayon.

5 ▬▬▶ green

6 ▬▬▶ red

7 ▬▬▶ blue

8 ▬▬▶ orange

9 ▬▬▶ purple

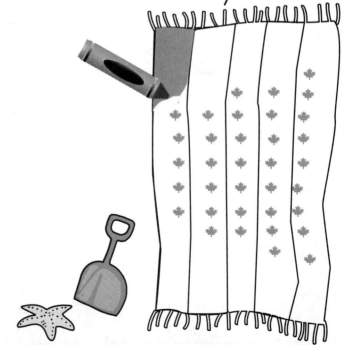

Count the maple leaves. Fill in the blanks.

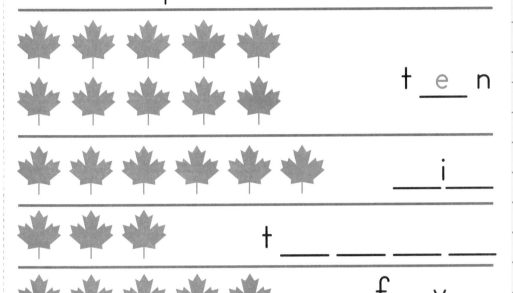

0	= zero
1	= one
2	= two
3	= three
4	= four
5	= five
6	= six
7	= seven
8	= eight
9	= nine
10	= ten

t _e_ n

___ i ___

t __ __ __ __

f __ v __

o __ __

e __ g __ __

z __ __ __

n __ __ e

t __ __

s __ v e __

3

Add:

Example:

$1 + 3 =$ ___4___ $4 + 1 =$ ___

$3 + 1 =$ ___ $2 + 1 =$ ___

$2 + 2 =$ ___ $3 + 2 =$ ___

$3 + 0 =$ ___ $1 + 4 =$ ___

Number and Quantity

Say each number.

Draw the matching number of objects in each box.

Example:

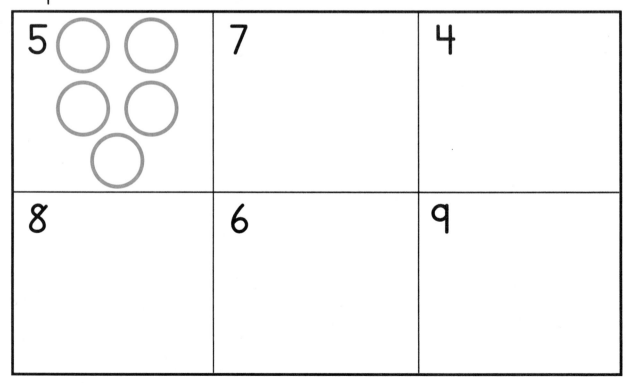

5 ○○ ○○ ○	7	4
8	6	9

Subtract. Try using counters to help.

2 ⬤⬤ －1 = [1]

3 ⬤⬤⬤ －1 = [ ]

4 ⬤⬤⬤⬤ －2 = [ ]

Draw your own counters for these ones.

5 －3 = [ ]

4 －3 = [ ]

3 －3 = [ ]

Recording Numbers 1 to 50 - Challenge

Print missing numbers in the boxes.

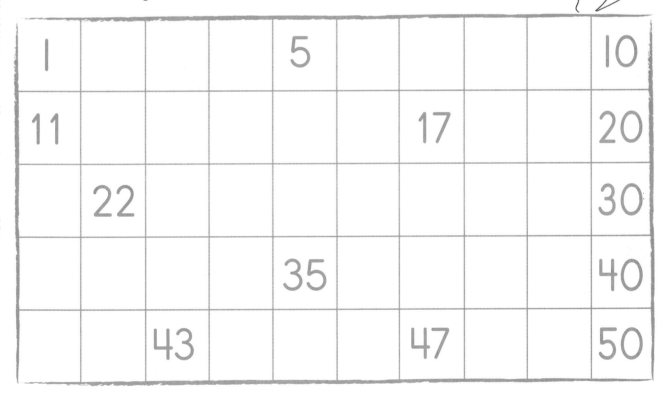

1				5					10
11						17			20
	22								30
				35					40
		43				47			50

Greater than   Less than

> **>**   **<**

(Hint: The open side of the symbol points to the greater number.)

3 hotdogs

Which is greater?
3 is less than 5,
so we write:
3 < 5

5 hotdogs

Write the numbers and > or <.

____3__ ⊙ __2____

___ ◯ ___

___ ◯ ___

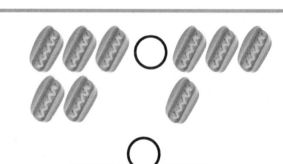

___ ◯ ___

Write > or < in the ◯. The number line can help.

9 ⊙ 2   4 ◯ 1   8 ◯ 7   2 ◯ 5

8 ◯ 5   1 ◯ 3   3 ◯ 5   6 ◯ 2

1 2 3 4 5 6 7 8 9 10

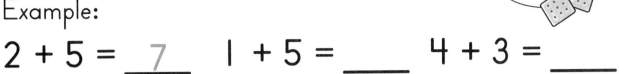

Add.

Example:

2 + 5 = _7_   1 + 5 = ___   4 + 3 = ___

1 + 6 = ___   6 + 2 = ___   0 + 8 = ___

5 + 3 = ___   2 + 7 = ___   3 + 4 = ___

7 + 1 = ___   1 + 8 = ___   6 + 3 = ___

4 + 5 = ___   3 + 7 = ___   5 + 5 = ___

Number Sequencing

Print the numbers that are missing.

1   2   3   4   5   _6_   ___   8

5   6   7   ___   ___   10   ___   ___

9   10   11   ___   ___   14   ___   16

15   ___   17   ___   ___   20   ___   22

22   ___   ___   ___   26   ___   ___   ___

Print the missing numbers.

1 2 3 ___ ___ 6 7 8 ___ ___ 11 12 ___ ___ 15

___ 17 18 ___ ___ 21 ___ 23 24 ___ ___ 27 ___ ___

30 31 32 ___ ___ 35 ___ 37 ___ ___ 40 ___ 42 ___

Addition

Add.

3	9	9	6	5	0	4	4	5	3
+5	+1	+2	+2	+5	+4	+5	+2	+4	+6
◯	◯	◯	◯	◯	◯	◯	◯	◯	◯

Number Sequencing

Print the number that goes before.

| 11 , 12, 13 | ___ ,7, 8 | ___ , 1 , 2 |

Print the number that goes between.

| 6, ___ , 8 | 9, ___ , 11 | 17, ___ , 19 |

Print the number that goes after.

| 8, 9, ___ | 14, 15, ___ | 18, 19, ___ |

8

Subtract.

8	5	9	9	9	6	9	5	8	7	7	6
−4	−4	−8	−6	−4	−3	−2	−3	−5	−3	−4	−4

Comparing Numbers

Circle the number that is greater.

(8)   6   17   20   18   16

Circle the number that is less.

21 (12)   18   14   8   0

Print missing numbers in the boxes.

51	52								
									100

Addition Facts

Add.

$$\begin{array}{r} 5 \\ +1 \\ \hline \end{array} \qquad \begin{array}{r} 2 \\ +3 \\ \hline \end{array} \qquad \begin{array}{r} 4 \\ +1 \\ \hline \end{array} \qquad \begin{array}{r} 2 \\ +2 \\ \hline \end{array} \qquad \begin{array}{r} 3 \\ +2 \\ \hline \end{array} \qquad \begin{array}{r} 2 \\ +1 \\ \hline \end{array}$$

$$\begin{array}{r} 1 \\ +4 \\ \hline \end{array} \qquad \begin{array}{r} 3 \\ +1 \\ \hline \end{array} \qquad \begin{array}{r} 3 \\ +4 \\ \hline \end{array} \qquad \begin{array}{r} 4 \\ +2 \\ \hline \end{array} \qquad \begin{array}{r} 5 \\ +0 \\ \hline \end{array} \qquad \begin{array}{r} 4 \\ +4 \\ \hline \end{array}$$

$$\begin{array}{r} 3 \\ +0 \\ \hline \end{array} \qquad \begin{array}{r} 2 \\ +4 \\ \hline \end{array} \qquad \begin{array}{r} 3 \\ +5 \\ \hline \end{array} \qquad \begin{array}{r} 2 \\ +5 \\ \hline \end{array} \qquad \begin{array}{r} 4 \\ +5 \\ \hline \end{array}$$

Print the missing numbers. Then touch each number and say it out loud.

1	2		4	5	6	7		9	10
11		13	14	15			18		
	22	23			26	27		29	
31		33	34		36		38		40
	42	43		45		47		49	
51			54	55			58		60
	62	63			66	67			
71			74	75			78	79	80
		83			86	87			90
91	92		94	95			98	99	

Subtraction Facts

Subtract.

$$\begin{array}{r} 6 \\ -1 \\ \hline \end{array} \quad \begin{array}{r} 4 \\ -2 \\ \hline \end{array} \quad \begin{array}{r} 3 \\ -1 \\ \hline \end{array} \quad \begin{array}{r} 1 \\ -1 \\ \hline \end{array} \quad \begin{array}{r} 5 \\ -2 \\ \hline \end{array} \quad \begin{array}{r} 4 \\ -1 \\ \hline \end{array}$$

For each pair, circle the number that is more.

Example:

⟨23⟩ 13	72 70	24 14
49 50	19 21	92 89

For each pair, circle the number that is less.

Example:

42 ⟨24⟩	56 65	11 17
32 43	82 28	21 51

Subtraction Facts

Subtract.

6 – 4 = ____   10 – 4 = ____   9 – 2 = ____

8 – 4 = ____   7 – 3 = ____   9 – 6 = ____

8 – 5 = ____   9 – 3 = ____   6 – 2 = ____

7 – 5 = ____   6 – 5 = ____   7 – 1 = ____

6 – 3 = ____   9 – 0 = ____   4 – 2 = ____

7 – 4 = ____   10 – 6 = ____   8 – 2 = ____

For each set of base ten blocks, count the number of tens and ones and write it on the line.

 ___2___ tens _____ ones

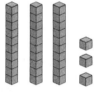 _____ tens _____ ones

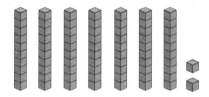 _____ tens _____ ones

Addition and Subtraction

Add or subtract. Watch the signs!

6 + 3 = _____   2 + 7 = _____   7 + 2 = _____

9 - 7 = _____   1 + 6 = _____   7 - 2 = _____

8 - 3 = _____   4 - 3 = _____   9 + 1 = _____

4 + 3 = _____   7 + 3 = _____   3 + 7 = _____

5 + 4 = _____   9 - 4 = _____   8 - 6 = _____

Count the wheels on the bikes by 2s.

Count the sandals by 2s.

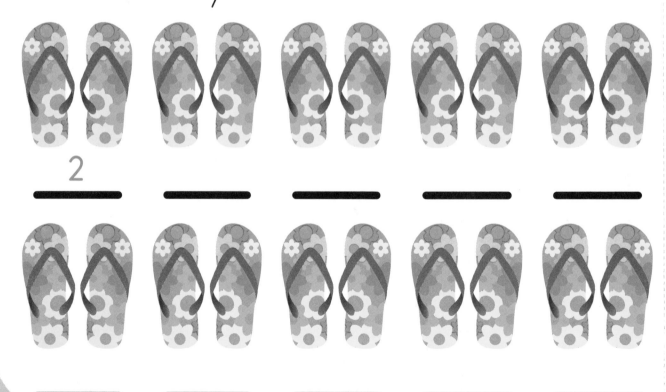

2

Look at the coins. Say their names.

   5¢   five cents   nickel

   10¢   ten cents   dime

   25¢   twenty-five cents   quarter

Place Value

How many tens and how many ones make up each number? One is done for you.

12 = ___1___ tens and ___2___ ones

24 = _____ tens and _____ ones

51 = _____ tens and _____ ones

37 = _____ tens and _____ ones

42 = _____ tens and _____ ones

70 = _____ tens and _____ ones

19 = _____ tens and _____ ones

91 = _____ tens and _____ ones

1 = _____ tens and _____ ones

100 = _____ tens and _____ ones

equals 1 ten

equals 1 one

Add or subtract with doubles. Watch the signs.

0	1	2	3	4	5	6
+0	+1	+2	+3	+4	+5	+6
(0)	◯	◯	◯	◯	◯	◯

0	1	2	3	4	5	6
−0	−1	−2	−3	−4	−5	−6
◯	◯	◯	◯	◯	◯	◯

Counting by 5s

Count the fingers by 5s.

5 ___ ___ ___ ___ ___

___ ___ ___ ___ ___

Count out loud.

5, 10, 15, 20, 25, 30, 35, 40, 45,

50, 55, 60, 65, 70, 75, 80, 85,

90, 95, 100

Each nickel is worth 5 cents (¢).
Count each row of nickels. Print the total number of cents on the line.

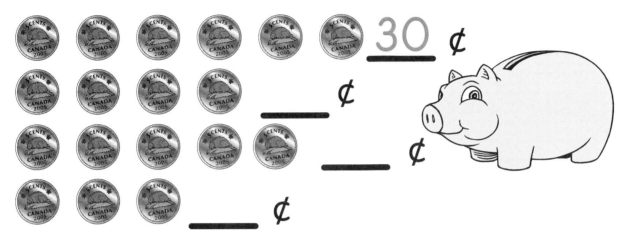

30 ¢

____ ¢

____ ¢

____ ¢

Number Sequencing

Write the number that comes after.

24, 25   42, ____   63, ____   34, ____

Write the number that comes before.

95, 96   ____, 48   ____, 35   ____, 50

Write the number that comes in between.

16, 17, 18   62, ____, 64   59, ____, 61

Write the numbers that come before and after.

16, 17, 18   ____, 42, ____   ____, 65, ____

How much is in each piggy bank?

5 ¢

___ ¢

___ ¢

___ ¢

___ ¢

___ ¢

Adding Three Numbers

Add. The first one has a hint to help you.

2 ⮌6	3	1	4	4	5
4 ⮌	1	8	5	3	2
+5	+7	+4	+3	+3	+3
11					

Each dime is worth 10 cents (¢). Count each row of dimes. Print the total number of cents on the line.

__60__ ¢

_____ ¢

_____ ¢

_____ ¢

Counting by 2s, 5s, 10s

Count out loud. Write the missing numbers.

2, 4, 6, ___, 10, ___, ___, 16, ___, 20, ___, 24, ___

28, ___, ___, 34, ___, ___, ___, 42, ___, ___, ___, 50

5, 10, 15, ___, ___, 30, ___, ___, ___, 50, ___, ___,

65, ___, ___, 80, ___, ___, ___, 100

10, ___, 30, ___, ___, 60, ___, ___, ___, 100

Count the change in each wallet.

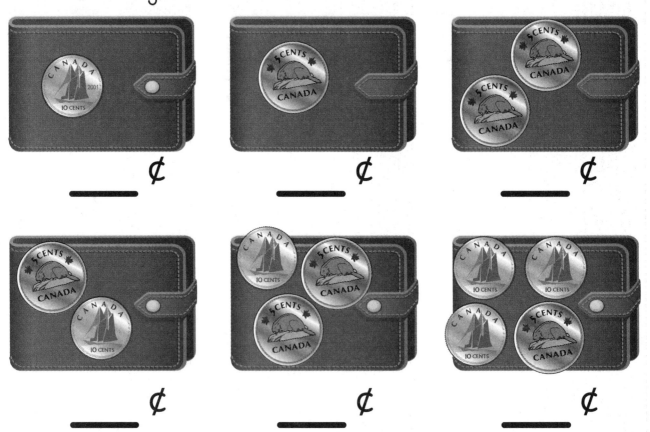

_____ ¢   _____ ¢   _____ ¢

_____ ¢   _____ ¢   _____ ¢

Place Value

Colour the box that shows the matching number.

Example:

3 tens 2 ones	**32**	5 tens 3 ones	36
	12		53
6 tens 4 ones	64	7 tens 1 ones	71
	28		17
4 tens 7 ones	41	3 tens 0 ones	30
	47		10

Point to each number as you count backwards.

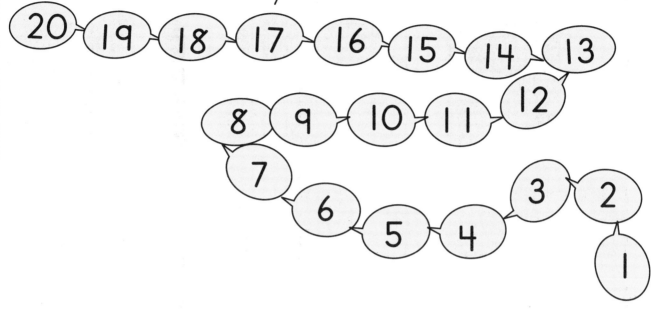

Money - Counting Loonies and Toonies

Count the money. Print the total on the line.

A loonie is $1.00   A toonie is $2.00

$ _____

$ _____

Count the wheels by 2s.

2 _____ _____ _____ _____

Count the toes by 5s.

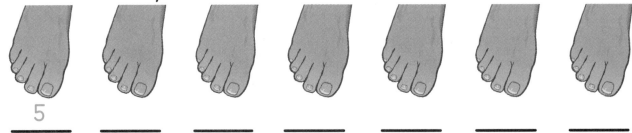

5 _____ _____ _____ _____ _____ _____

Count the fingers by 10s.

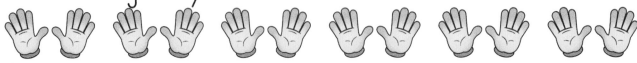

_____ _____ _____ _____ _____

Solving Word Problems

One has 4 balloons and the other has 6 balloons.
How many balloons all together?

One has 6 trains and the other has 3 trains.
How many trains all together?

_____

_____

Add or subtract.

Match the answer to the colour in the key.

Colour the picture.

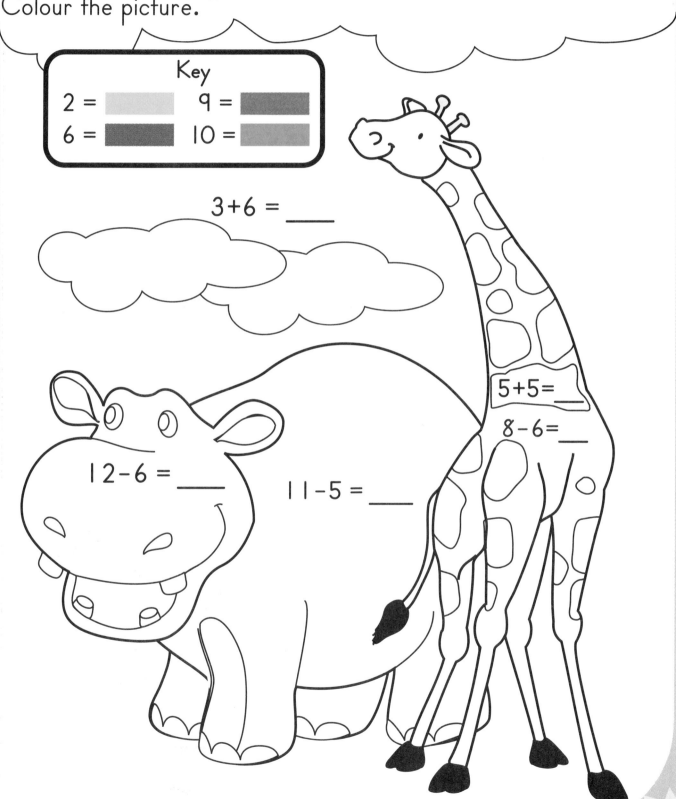

Key

2 =

6 =

9 =

10 =

3+6 = ___

5+5= ___

8−6= ___

12−6 = ___

11−5 = ___

Ordinal numbers tell what order things are in.

first	second	third	fourth	fifth	sixth	seventh	eighth	ninth	tenth
1st	2nd	3rd	4th	5th	6th	7th	8th	9th	10th

Colour the fourth hat red. Colour the sixth hat green.

Colour the first hat blue. Colour the tenth hat green.

Colour the eighth mitt yellow. Colour the second mitt orange.

Colour the seventh mitt yellow. Colour the fifth mitt purple.

There are 8 toys in the toy box. Some belong to Max and some belong to Dax. Max has 2 more toys in the box than Dax.

How many toys does Max have in the box? _____

Addition and Subtraction

Add or subtract. Watch the signs!

8	9	7	4	6	6
+4	+6	−3	+5	+4	−3
◯	◯	◯	◯	◯	◯

8	12	19	17	7	8
−3	+6	−7	−3	+4	−4
◯	◯	◯	◯	◯	◯

Add or subtract.

7	8	9	6
+4	+6	-3	+5

$11 - 2 =$ ___

$14 - 6 =$ ___

$13 - 5 =$ ___

$17 - 1 =$ ___

Money

How many of each coin are in the piggy bank?
Write it on the line.

_____ nickels   _____ quarters

_____ dimes   _____ loonies

_____ toonies

This pizza has two equal parts. Each part is $\frac{1}{2}$ of the whole.

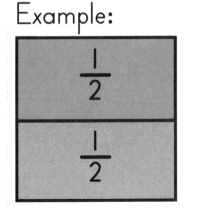

Write $\frac{1}{2}$ on both parts of each shape.
Then colour $\frac{1}{2}$ of each shape red.
Colour the other $\frac{1}{2}$ blue.

Example:

| $\frac{1}{2}$ |
| $\frac{1}{2}$ |

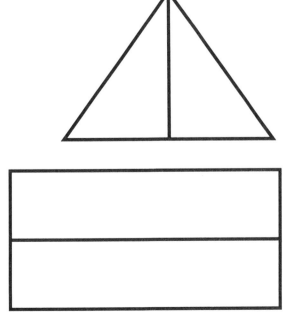

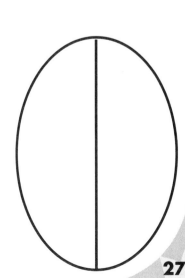

This pizza has three equal parts.
Each part is $\frac{1}{3}$ of the whole.

Write $\frac{1}{3}$ on each part of each shape.
Then colour $\frac{1}{3}$ of each shape red,
$\frac{1}{3}$ blue, and $\frac{1}{3}$ yellow.

This pizza has four equal parts.
Each part is $\frac{1}{4}$ of the whole.

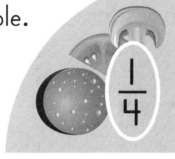 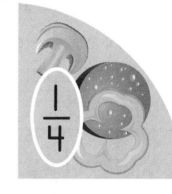

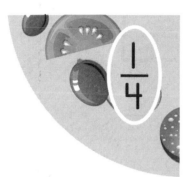 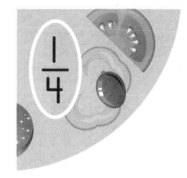

Write $\frac{1}{4}$ on each part of each shape.
Then colour $\frac{1}{4}$ of each shape red, $\frac{1}{4}$ blue,
$\frac{1}{4}$ yellow, and $\frac{1}{4}$ green.

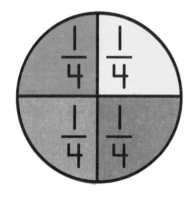

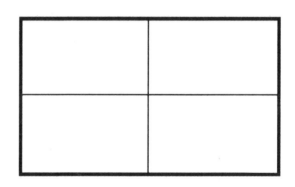

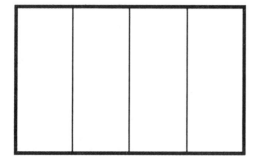

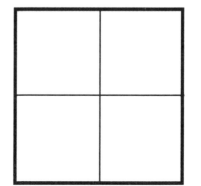

Colour only the shapes that show halves.

Put an X on the pictures that do NOT show halves.

Example:

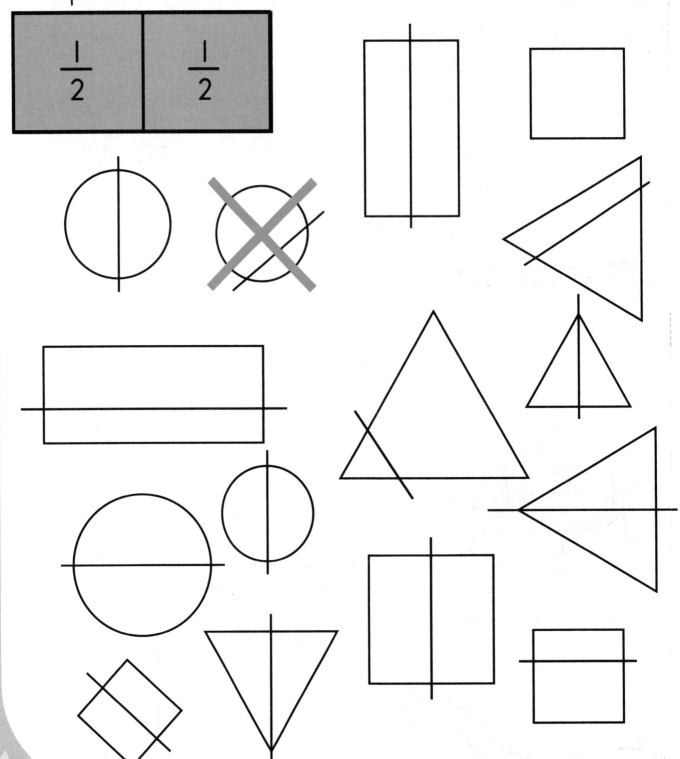

Use a paperclip  to measure things.

 _____2_____ paperclips

 _____ paperclips

 _____ paperclips

_____ paperclips

Using Standard Units

Use a ruler to measure things.

 _____5_____ cm

 _____ cm

 _____ cm

 _____ cm

Colour the minute hand (long) red.
Colour the hour hand (short) green.
Print the numbers on the clock.

1   2   3   4   5   6   7   8   9   10   11   12

The short hand points to 3.

The long hand points to 12.
It is 3 o'clock or 3:00.

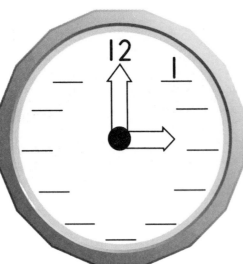

This number tells the hour. It is 3:00.

This number tells the minutes after the hour.

Telling Time to the Hour

What time does each clock say? Write the time on the line.
(Hint: The minute hand is long and hour hand is short.)

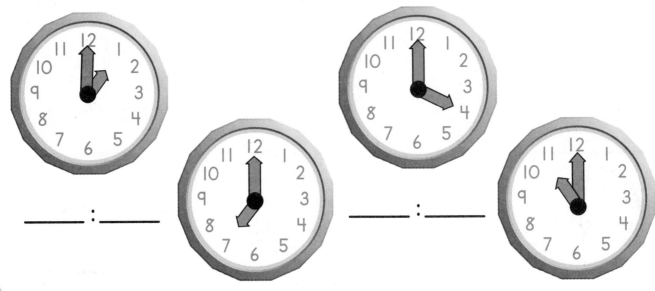

_____ : _____

_____ : _____

_____ : _____

_____ : _____

Colour the minute hand (long) red.
Colour the hour hand (short) green.

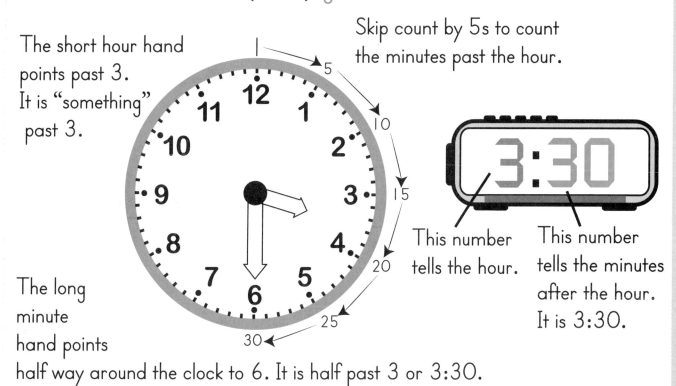

The short hour hand points past 3.
It is "something" past 3.

Skip count by 5s to count the minutes past the hour.

This number tells the hour.

This number tells the minutes after the hour. It is 3:30.

The long minute hand points half way around the clock to 6. It is half past 3 or 3:30.

Telling Time to the Half Hour

What time does each clock say? Write the time on the line.

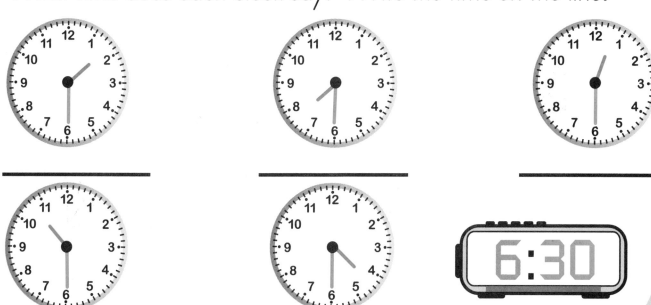

Months have 30 or 31 days, except February, which has 28 or 29 days.

July

Sunday	Monday	Tuesday	Wednesday	Thursday	Friday	Saturday
	1	2	3	4	5	6
7	8	9	10	11	12	13
14	15	16	17	18	19	20
21	22	23	24	25	26	27
28	29	30	31			

Use the calendar above to answer the questions.

1. Canada's birthday is on July 1st.

    What day of the week is Canada Day on?_____

2. How many Mondays are in July?_____

3. Mary has a play date on July 19th. Today is July 16th.

    How many days until her play date ?_____

4. What month comes after July?_____

Draw a line from each object to the matching shape.

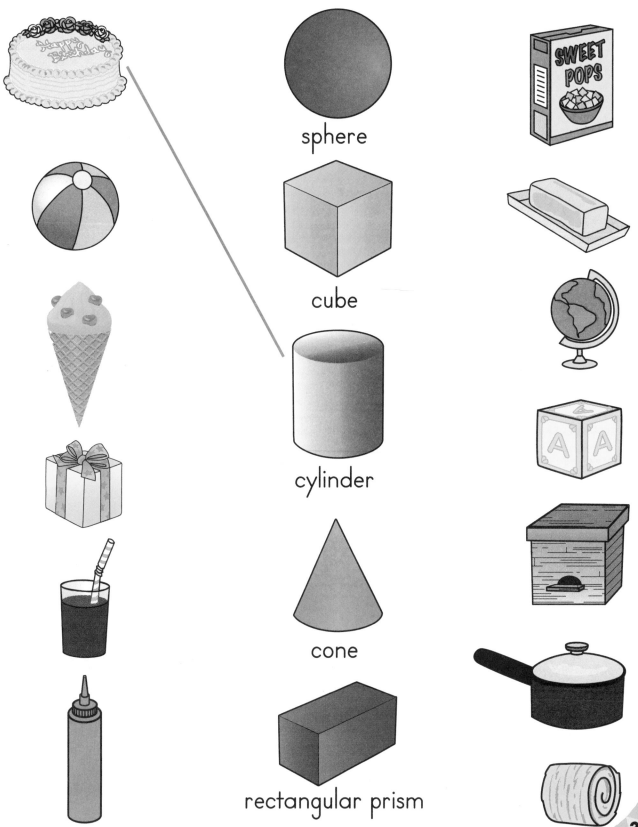

sphere

cube

cylinder

cone

rectangular prism

Draw the shapes that continue each pattern.

ABCABCABC ___ ___ ___

Identify the Core

These three items repeat to create a pattern. They are called the **core**.

Circle the **core** of each pattern.

Look at the picture graph. Answer the questions.

Favourite Snacks in Ms. Bertin's Class

Fruit	🍎	🍎	🍎	
Granola Bars	🍫	🍫	🍫	🍫
Vegetables	🥕	🥕		
Cheese and Crackers	🧀			

Each snack represents 1 child.

How many children like fruit best? _____
How many children like granola bars best? _____
How many children like vegetables best? _____
How many children like cheese and crackers best? _____

More children like granola bars best than like cheese and crackers best. How many more? _____
(Hint: Use subtraction.)

How many children in all voted for their favourite snack?

_____

Decide whether each picture is **likely** or **unlikely**.
Circle the word you chose.

likely   unlikely

likely   unlikely

likely   unlikely

likely   unlikely

Sequencing

Number the pictures to show the correct order.

Solutions

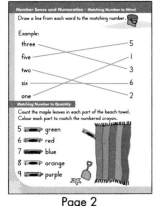

Page 2

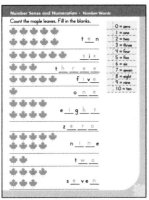

Page 3

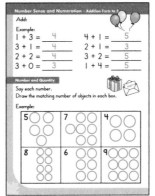

Page 4

Page 5

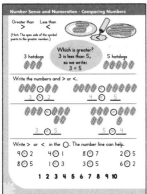

Page 6

Page 7

Page 8

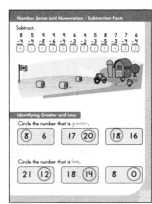

Page 9

Page 10

Page 11

Page 12

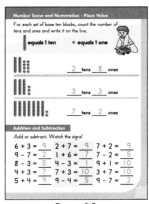

Page 13

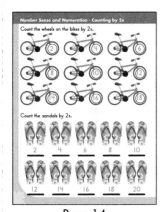

Page 14

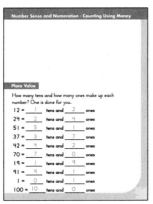

Page 15

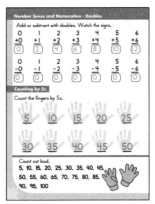

Page 16

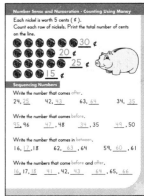

Page 17

Solutions

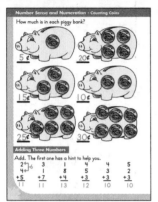

Page 18

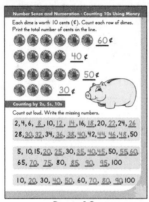

Page 19

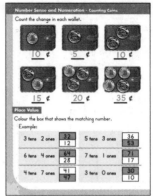

Page 20

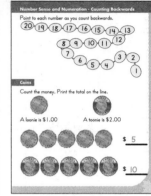

Page 21

Page 22

Page 23

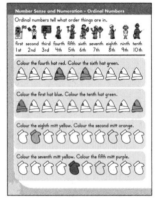

Page 24

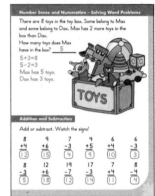

Page 25

Page 26

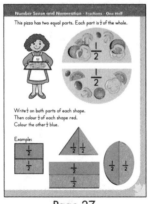

Page 27

Page 28

Page 29

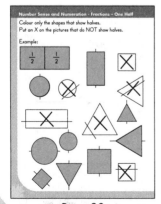

Page 30

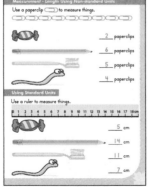

Page 31

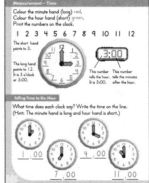

Page 32

Page 33